Collins

AQA GCSE Sociology

Sociology

Workbook

AQA GCSE 9-1

Workbook

Pauline Wilson

Revision Tips

Rethink Revision

Have you ever taken part in a quiz and thought '*I know this*!', but, despite frantically racking your brain, you just couldn't come up with the answer?

It's very frustrating when this happens, but in a fun situation it doesn't really matter. However, in your GCSE exams, it will be essential that you can recall the relevant information quickly when you need to.

Most students think that revision is about making sure you **know** *stuff*. Of course, this is important, but it is also about becoming confident that you can **retain** that *stuff* over time and **recall** it quickly when needed.

Revision That Really Works

Experts have discovered that there are two techniques that help with all of these things and consistently produce better results in exams compared to other revision techniques.

Applying these techniques to your GCSE revision will ensure you get better results in your exams and will have all the relevant knowledge at your fingertips when you start studying for further qualifications, like AS and A Levels, or begin work.

It really isn't rocket science either – you simply need to:

- **test yourself** on each topic as many times as possible
- **leave a gap** between the test sessions.

It is most effective if you leave a good period of time between the test sessions, e.g. between a week and a month. The idea is that just as you start to forget the information, you force yourself to recall it again, keeping it fresh in your mind.

Three Essential Revision Tips

1. **Use Your Time Wisely**
   - Allow yourself plenty of time.
   - Try to start revising six months before your exams – it's more effective and less stressful.
   - Your revision time is precious so use it wisely – using the techniques described on this page will ensure you revise effectively and efficiently and get the best results.
   - Don't waste time re-reading the same information over and over again – it's time-consuming and not effective!

2. **Make a Plan**
   - Identify all the topics you need to revise.
   - Plan at least five sessions for each topic.
   - One hour should be ample time to test yourself on the key ideas for a topic.
   - Spread out the practice sessions for each topic – the optimum time to leave between each session is about one month but, if this isn't possible, just make the gaps as big as realistically possible.

3. **Test Yourself**
   - Methods for testing yourself include: quizzes, practice questions, flashcards, past papers, explaining a topic to someone else, etc.
   - Don't worry if you get an answer wrong – provided you check what the correct answer is, you are more likely to get the same or similar questions right in future!

Visit our website for more information about the benefits of these revision techniques and for further guidance on how to plan ahead and make them work for you.

www.collins.co.uk/collinsGCSErevision

Contents

Families

Different Family Forms

1 Which term is commonly used by sociologists to describe families in which one or both partners have a child or children from a previous relationship living with them?
Shade **one** box only. [1]

A Extended ⭕

B Symmetrical ⭕

C Empty nest ⭕

D Reconstituted ⭕

2 Describe **one** example of global diversity in families. [3]

....

....

....

....

....

....

....

....

Families

The Functions of Families

3 Discuss how far sociologists agree that the nuclear family is an essential part of British society today.

[12]

....

....

....

....

....

....

....

....

....

....

....

....

....

....

....

....

....

Continue your answer on a separate piece of paper.

Families

The Marxist Perspective on Families

4 Identify and explain **one** advantage of using group interviews to investigate married people's attitudes towards marriage and family life. [4]

....

....

....

....

....

....

....

....

....

....

Feminist and Other Critical Views of Families

5 Describe **one** example of inequality in power relationships between family members. [3]

....

....

....

....

....

....

Families

Conjugal Role Relationships

6 Identify and explain **one** advantage of using secondary sources to investigate family life in Britain today.

[4]

....

....

....

....

....

....

....

....

....

7 Describe the instrumental role in nuclear families.

[3]

....

....

....

....

....

....

....

Families

Changing Relationships Within Families

8 Identify and explain **one** disadvantage of using a social survey to investigate the quality of parenting.

[4]

Changing Family and Household Structures

9 Describe **one** example of a household in Britain today.

[3]

Families

Marriage and Divorce

10 Which term is used by sociologists to describe a marriage in which a wife has two or more husbands at the same time? Shade **one** box only. [1]

A Polygamy ⬜   **B** Polyandry ⬜

C Polygyny ⬜   **D** Monogamy ⬜

11 Identify **one** possible consequence of divorce for the former partners and explain how you would investigate this consequence using unstructured interviews. [4]

....

....

....

....

....

....

....

....

....

....

....

....

12 Which term is used by sociologists to describe the process by which religion loses significance in society? Shade **one** box only. [1]

A Idealisation ⬜   **B** Alienation ⬜

C Privatisation ⬜   **D** Secularisation ⬜

Education

The Role of Education from a Functionalist Perspective

1 Identify **one** function of the education system and explain how you would investigate this function using observation. [4]

_____

_____

_____

_____

_____

_____

_____

_____

_____

The Marxist Approach to Education

2 Describe the correspondence principle in education as outlined by Bowles and Gintis. [3]

_____

_____

_____

_____

_____

_____

_____

Education

3. Discuss how far sociologists agree that the main role of the education system is to produce a workforce for capitalism.

[12]

_____

_____

_____

_____

_____

_____

_____

_____

_____

_____

_____

_____

_____

_____

_____

_____

_____

Continue your answer on a separate piece of paper.

Education

Different Types of School

4 Describe **one** example of a type of secondary school in Britain today. [3]

....

....

....

....

....

....

....

5 Which term is used by sociologists to describe a type of school that is designed to cater for students of all abilities? Shade **one** box only. [1]

A Comprehensive school ⬜○   **B** Grammar school ⬜○

C State school ⬜○   **D** Public school ⬜○

6 Describe the tripartite system of education. [3]

....

....

....

....

....

....

....

Education

Social Class and Educational Achievement

7 Describe **one** home-based factor that could influence students' performance at school. [3]

....

....

....

....

....

....

....

The Impact of School Processes on Working-Class Students' Achievements

8 Identify and explain **one** advantage of using a longitudinal study to investigate the effects of banding in schools. [4]

....

....

....

....

....

....

....

....

....

....

Education

Ethnicity and Educational Achievement

9 Which term is commonly used by sociologists to describe a curriculum that is biased towards white, European culture? Shade **one** box only. [1]

A Gendered curriculum ◯

B Biased curriculum ◯

C Ethnocentric curriculum ◯

D Informal curriculum ◯

Gender and Educational Achievement

10 Describe the crisis in masculinity that may be experienced by some males. [3]

Education

11 Which term is used by sociologists to describe the study of people in everyday settings?
Shade **one** box only.   [1]

A   Ethnography   ◯

B   Cross-cultural study   ◯

C   Cohort study   ◯

D   One-shot survey   ◯

12 Identify **one** ethical issue that you would need to consider when investigating sub-cultures in
a school and explain how you would deal with this issue in your investigation.   [4]

....

....

....

....

....

....

....

....

....

....

Crime and Deviance

An Introduction to Crime and Deviance

1 Identify **one** agency of informal social control and explain how you would investigate this agency using unstructured interviews. [4]

....

....

....

....

....

....

....

....

....

....

2 Describe **one** example of an agency of formal social control. [3]

....

....

....

....

....

....

Crime and Deviance

3 Identify and explain **one** advantage of using a longitudinal study to investigate deviant careers. [4]

....

....

....

....

....

....

....

....

....

....

....

4 What term is used by sociologists to describe the breakdown of norms in society?
Shade **one** box only. [1]

A Alienation ⃝   **B** Moral panic ⃝

C Anomie ⃝   **D** Deviancy amplification ⃝

Marxist and Feminist Explanations of Crime and Deviance

5 Describe **one** way in which some females may be controlled within the home. [3]

....

....

....

....

....

....

Continue your answer on a separate piece of paper.

Crime and Deviance

Statistical Data on the Extent of Crime

6 Describe the dark figure of crime. [3]

Factors Affecting Criminal and Deviant Behaviour

7 Identify **one** ethical issue that you would need to consider when investigating a deviant sub-culture and explain how you would deal with this issue in your investigation. [4]

Crime and Deviance

Other Factors Affecting Criminal and Deviant Behaviour

8 Describe the class deal that may be experienced by some women. [3]

....

....

....

....

....

....

....

....

....

....

9 What term is used by sociologists to describe the more lenient treatment of female offenders within the criminal justice system? Shade **one** box only. [1]

A Chivalry thesis ◯

B Double deviancy thesis ◯

C Institutional sexism ◯

D Gender stereotyping ◯

Crime and Deviance

10 Discuss how far sociologists agree that social classes in Britain today have different experiences of the criminal justice system.

[12]

....

....

....

....

....

....

....

....

....

....

....

....

....

....

....

....

Continue your answer on a separate piece of paper.

The Media and Public Debates over Crime

11 What term is used by sociologists to describe a group that is defined as a threat to society's values? Shade **one** box only.

[1]

A Folk devil	○	**B** Gatekeeper	○
C Deviant	○	**D** Delinquent	○

Social Stratification

An Introduction to Social Stratification

1 What term is commonly used by sociologists to describe the uneven distribution of resources (such as income or power) or opportunities related to, for instance, education and health? Shade **one** box only.

[1]

A Social class ⭕

B Social stratification ⭕

C Social inequality ⭕

D Social status ⭕

Different Views of Social Class

2 Which term is commonly used by sociologists to describe how people see themselves in social class terms? Shade **one** box only.

[1]

A Objective class ⭕

B Subjective class ⭕

C Class alignment ⭕

D False class consciousness ⭕

Factors Affecting Life Chances

3 Describe the glass ceiling in the workplace.

[3]

....

....

....

....

....

....

....

....

Social Stratification

4 Describe **one** way in which governments have tried to address racial discrimination in the labour market.

[3]

....

....

....

....

....

....

....

5 Identify and describe **one** agency of gender socialisation.

[3]

....

....

....

....

....

....

....

....

Social Stratification

6 Identify **one** type of social mobility and explain how you would investigate this type using questionnaires. [4]

_____

_____

_____

_____

_____

_____

_____

_____

_____

_____

_____

7 Which term is used by sociologists to describe a process in which affluent working-class families are becoming middle class in their norms and values? Shade **one** box only. [1]

A Proletarianisation ⬜   B Embourgeoisement ⬜

C Alienation ⬜   D Class dealignment ⬜

8 Which term is used by sociologists to describe a family whose lifestyle and social relationships focus on the home and immediate family? Shade **one** box only. [1]

A Modified extended family ⬜   B Symmetrical family ⬜

C Patriarchal family ⬜   D Privatised nuclear family ⬜

Social Stratification

Wealth, Income and Poverty

9 Identify and explain **one** disadvantage of using official statistics to investigate poverty in the UK. [4]

_____

_____

_____

_____

_____

_____

_____

_____

_____

_____

_____

_____

10 Which term is used by sociologists to describe the state of poverty in which people see themselves as living in poverty? Shade **one** box only. [1]

A Subjective poverty ⬜ **B** Objective poverty ⬜

C Culture of poverty ⬜ **D** Welfare dependency ⬜

11 Which term is used by sociologists to describe the experience of being shut out from participation in everyday activities and customs that most people take for granted? Shade **one** box only. [1]

A Environmental poverty ⬜ **B** Relative deprivation ⬜

C Social exclusion ⬜ **D** Poverty trap ⬜

Social Stratification

Different Explanations of Poverty

12 Discuss how far sociologists agree that rising divorce rates are the most important reason for child poverty in the UK.

[12]

Continue your answer on a separate piece of paper.

Social Stratification

Power and Authority

13 Identify and explain **one** patriarchal structure highlighted by the sociologist Sylvia Walby.   [4]

Power and the State

14 Describe **one** example of an institution of the state in the UK.   [3]

Collins

GCSE Sociology
Paper 1 The Sociology of Families and Education

Time allowed: 1 hour 45 minutes

The maximum mark for this paper is 100.

Instructions

- Use black ink or black ball-point pen.
- Answer **all** questions.
- You must answer the questions in the spaces provided. Do **not** write outside the box around each page or on blank pages.
- Do all rough work in this book.

Information

- The marks for questions are shown in brackets.
- Questions should be answered in continuous prose. You will be assessed on your ability to:
  - use good English
  - organise information clearly
  - use specialist vocabulary where appropriate.

Name: ....

Section A: Families
Answer **all** questions in this section.

---

0 1 Which term is commonly used by sociologists to describe the shame or disgrace attached to particular behaviour? Shade **one** box only.

A   Social exclusion   ◯

B   Social convention   ◯

C   Social stigma   ◯

D   Double standards   ◯   **[1 mark]**

0 2 Which term is used to describe the criminal offence of marrying when already married to someone else? Shade **one** box only.

A   Bigamy   ◯

B   Serial monogamy   ◯

C   Polygamy   ◯

D   Empty shell marriage   ◯   **[1 mark]**

0 3 Describe an empty nest family.   **[3 marks]**

....

....

....

....

....

....

....

0 4 Identify and describe **one** example of a dependent family member.   **[3 marks]**

Item A

Data from the Office for National Statistics (ONS) shows that, in 1973, there were 8.4 divorces per 1000 married men and 8.4 per 1000 married women in England and Wales. In general, the divorce rate increased over the next 20 years and, in 1993, the figures stood at 14.3 for men and 14.1 for women.

In 2013, however, there were just 9.8 divorces per 1000 married men and 9.8 per 1000 married women. These rates are similar to the divorce rates in the mid-1970s.

0 5 From **Item A**, examine **one** strength of research using official statistics on divorce.   **[2 marks]**

0 6 Identify and explain **one** factor that may have led to an increase in the divorce rate between 1973 and 1993, as referred to in **Item A**.　　　　　　　　**[4 marks]**

0 7 Identify and explain **one** advantage of using a focus group to investigate arranged marriage in Britain.　　　　　　　　**[4 marks]**

....

....

....

....

....

....

Item B

> In her article on conventional families, Ann Oakley (1982) drew on evidence from research carried out by other sociologists. She argues that conventional nuclear family life is no longer the norm in statistical terms. Yet the idea of the conventional family is still a powerful one in society. People expect conventional family life to bring them happiness.
>
> However, Oakley argues that there are strains beneath the surface. This is seen, for example, in the health problems and depression experienced by family members.

0 8   From **Item B**, identify and describe the research method used by Ann Oakley, including what you know of her perspective on the family.   **[4 marks]**

....

....

....

....

....

....

....

....

0 9 Identify **one** type of family diversity and explain how you would investigate this type of diversity using unstructured interviews.   **[4 marks]**

....

1 0 Discuss how far sociologists agree that the family is the main source of gender inequality in British society today.   **[12 marks]**

....

....

....

....

....

....

....

....

....

....

1 **1** Discuss how far sociologists agree that the main function of the nuclear family in Britain today is the primary socialisation of children. **[12 marks]**

....

....

....

....

....

....

....

Practice Exam Paper 1

Turn over for the next question.

Practice Exam Paper 1

Section B: Education
Answer all questions in this section.

---

1 2 Which term is used by sociologists to describe research in which the participants are not aware that they are taking part in a study? Shade **one** box only.

A   Overt research   ◯

B   Covert research   ◯

C   Non-participant observation   ◯

D   Informed consent   ◯   **[1 mark]**

1 3 Which term is used by sociologists to describe the learning that takes place when people develop knowledge and skills by observing what is happening around them in everyday life? Shade **one** box only.

A   Official education   ◯

B   Official curriculum   ◯

C   Formal education   ◯

D   Informal education   ◯   **[1 mark]**

1 4 Describe the gendered curriculum in education.   **[3 marks]**

....

....

....

....

....

....

_____

_____

_____

1 5 Describe **one** example of a system of stratification based on achieved status. **[3 marks]**

_____

_____

_____

_____

_____

_____

_____

_____

Item C

In 2016, the Sutton Trust published a research report on young people receiving private tuition in England and Wales. The paper drew on a poll carried out by an opinion poll company for the Sutton Trust. The poll asked young people aged 11–16 years about the experience of receiving private tuition in England and Wales. The sample size was 2555 students.

The paper also drew on data from several other sources including the UK Millennium Cohort Study, which had a sample size of 19 000 children aged 11 years.

The Sutton Trust reported that affluent families were more likely to employ private tutors for their children than less affluent families. Children attending private schools were around twice as likely to have private tuition as children attending state schools. Ethnic minority students and girls were more likely to receive private tuition than white students and boys.

In England and Wales over the last decade, the proportion of young people who have received private tuition rose by seven percentage points, from 18 per cent to 25 per cent.

Some students received private tuition to improve their performance in entrance exams.

Practice Exam Paper 1

1 6 From **Item C**, examine **one** strength of the research. [2 marks]

_____

_____

_____

_____

_____

1 7 Identify and explain **one** possible reason why the proportion of young people who have received private tuition is rising. [4 marks]

_____

_____

_____

_____

_____

_____

_____

_____

_____

1 8 Identify and explain **one** disadvantage of using a snowball sample to investigate truancy among secondary school students.

[4 marks]

Item D

Stephen Ball studied the impact of banding on students' experiences of schooling in a mixed comprehensive school. He undertook an intensive case study of one school, observing lessons, participating in the school's daily life as a supply teacher and teaching some timetabled lessons as a regular teacher. The field work was carried out over a period of more than two years.

Ball took notes during his observation of lessons and wrote these up as transcripts. He also kept diary notes to record his observations.

1 9 From **Item D**, identify and describe the research method used by Ball, including what you know of his perspective on education.   **[4 marks]**

....

....

....

....

....

....

....

....

....

....

2 0 Identify **one** expectation that teachers might have of students in the top band and explain the possible impact of this expectation on students' educational achievements. **[4 marks]**

....

....

....

....

....

....

....

....

....

....

2 1 Discuss how far sociologists agree that students' family backgrounds are the most important factor in explaining differences in their educational achievements.　　**[12 marks]**

Turn over for the next question.

Practice Exam Paper 1

2 2 Discuss how far sociologists agree that feminism is the main reason for the improvements in the educational achievements of girls over the last 40 years. **[12 marks]**

End of questions

GCSE Sociology

Paper 2 The Sociology of Crime and Deviance and Social Stratification

Time allowed: 1 hour 45 minutes

The maximum mark for this paper is 100.

Instructions

- Use black ink or black ball-point pen.
- Answer **all** questions.
- You must answer the questions in the spaces provided. Do **not** write outside the box around each page or on blank pages.
- Do all rough work in this book.

Information

- The marks for questions are shown in brackets.
- Questions should be answered in continuous prose. You will be assessed on your ability to:
  - use good English
  - organise information clearly
  - use specialist vocabulary where appropriate.

Name: ....

Section A: Crime and Deviance
Answer **all** questions in this section.

0 1 What term is used by sociologists to describe the deal that offers women emotional and material rewards in return for living with a male breadwinner within a family? Shade **one** box only.

A Class deal ⬜

B Gender deal ⬜

C Double standards ⬜

D Dual-worker family ⬜ **[1 mark]**

0 2 What term is used by sociologists to describe a research method that involves collecting data through in-depth interviews with participants? Shade **one** box only.

A Questionnaire ⬜

B Structured interview ⬜

C Unstructured interview ⬜

D Participant observation ⬜ **[1 mark]**

0 3 Describe **one** example of an issue of public concern in the UK related to crime. **[3 marks]**

....

....

....

....

....

....

....

....

....

0 4 Describe agenda setting in the media with reference to crime. **[3 marks]**

....

....

....

....

....

....

....

....

....

....

Item A

Sociologists can help the authorities deal with football hooliganism by studying the people involved and what motivates them. Research suggests that most football hooligans are working-class males aged 18 to 24 years. John Williams, Eric Dunning and Patrick Murphy (1989) worked together on a project in the Department of Sociology at the University of Leicester that explored football hooliganism among English fans at away games in Europe. The fieldwork was based on three covert participant observation studies. John Williams carried out all three studies. This was because he was young enough, street wise enough and interested enough in football to be able to pass as an everyday English football fan. The researchers explored the norms and values of the youths and young men involved in football hooliganism.

0 5 From **Item A**, examine **one** strength of the research. [2 marks]

0 6 Identify and explain **one** factor that may have led young men to engage in football hooliganism, referred to as a concern in **Item A**. [4 marks]

0 7 Identify and explain **one** disadvantage of using a self-report study to investigate white-collar crime.

[4 marks]

Item B

Merton, a North American sociologist, explains crime and deviance in terms of the structure and culture of society rather than focusing on people's genes or personalities.

Merton argues that people's aspirations and goals (what they see as worth striving for) are largely determined by the values of their culture. The problem is that some individuals and groups accept the goal of achieving economic success but lack opportunities to succeed through legitimate (or socially acceptable) means. Some people end up experiencing strain between the goals they have been socialised to strive for and the means of achieving them.

In this situation, where there is a mismatch between goals and means, a condition of anomie (or normlessness) develops. In other words, the norms that regulate behaviour break down and people turn to whatever means work for them to achieve material success. When anomie develops anything goes, and high rates of crime and delinquency are likely.

Merton identifies five possible ways that individuals respond to success goals in society. Some of these responses (such as innovation, ritualism and retreatism) involve crime and deviance.

0 8 From **Item B,** identify and describe **one** response to success goals in society that Merton highlighted, including what you know of his perspective on crime and deviance. **[4 marks]**

....

....

....

....

....

....

....

....

....

....

0 9 Identify **one** ethical issue you would need to consider when investigating the victims of crime and explain how you would deal with this issue in your investigation. **[4 marks]**

....

....

....

....

....

....

....

....

....

....

....

1 0 Discuss how far sociologists agree that inadequate socialisation at home is the main reason for delinquency among young people. **[12 marks]**

....

....

....

....

....

....

....

....

....

....

1 | 1 | Discuss how far sociologists agree that police-recorded crime statistics do not accurately reflect the true level of female criminality. **[12 marks]**

Section B: Social Stratification
Answer **all** questions in this section.

1 2 What term is commonly used by sociologists to describe social positions that are fixed at birth? Shade **one** box only.

A Ascribed status   ○

B Achieved status   ○

C Monarchy   ○

D Social status   ○   **[1 mark]**

1 3 What term is used by sociologists to refer to government by the people? Shade **one** box only.

A Dictatorship   ○

B Democracy   ○

C Pluralism   ○

D Rational legal authority   ○   **[1 mark]**

1 4 Identify and describe **one** example of a social construct.   **[3 marks]**

....

....

....

....

....

....

| 1 | 5 | Describe the process of embourgeoisement that may be experienced by some affluent workers.

[3 marks]

_____

_____

_____

_____

_____

_____

_____

Item C

Irene Zempi and Neil Chakraborti (2014) studied the experiences of Muslim women who wear the niqab (a face-covering or veil) in public places in Leicester. The research was based on 60 semi-structured interviews with veiled Muslim women. In addition, one of the researchers, Irene Zempi (who describes herself as a white, Orthodox Christian woman) wore a veil in public places such as on public transport, in shopping centres and on the streets of Leicester for four weeks. This allowed her to understand more fully the women's experiences as victims of Islamophobia (hostility towards Muslims and Islam) in their daily lives.

For veiled Muslim women, the fear of being attacked and incidents of victimisation can have significant consequences, such as loss of confidence and depression. It can also limit Muslim women's movements, leading to social isolation.

1 6 From **Item C**, examine **one** strength of the research. [2 marks]

1 7 Identify and explain **one** way in which religious hate crime might affect people's life chances as experienced by many of the women referred to in **Item C**. [4 marks]

1 8 Identify and explain **one** disadvantage of using structured interviews to research people's experiences of racism in the UK.

[4 marks]

....

....

....

....

....

....

....

....

....

....

Item D

Peter Townsend (1979) investigated how many people were living in poverty in the UK, their characteristics and problems. He used a large-scale questionnaire survey and collected data on 2052 households and 6098 individuals. The national questionnaire survey covered household resources and standards of living.

Townsend calculated that almost 23 per cent of the population were in poverty. He identified particular groups of people who were at risk of poverty. These included elderly people who had worked in unskilled manual jobs, and children in families of young unskilled manual workers or in one-parent families.

1 9   From **Item D**, identify and describe the research method used by Peter Townsend, including what you know of his perspective on poverty.   **[4 marks]**

2 0 Identify **one** group that is at risk of poverty in the UK and explain why this particular group is at risk of poverty.

[4 marks]

....

....

....

....

....

....

....

....

....

....

2 1 Discuss how far sociologists agree that ethnicity is the most important source of inequality in British society today.
[12 marks]

Turn over for the next question.

2 2 Discuss how far sociologists agree that power is distributed widely in contemporary British society.

[12 marks]

End of questions

There are no questions printed on this page.

Answers

Different Family Forms

1. **D**
2. **Suggested answer:** Kibbutzim in Israel – in a kibbutz settlement, people have a collective way of life rather than living in privatised nuclear families. Originally, children lived together in children's houses and were brought up collectively, but today they are likely to live with their parents until they are teenagers. Meals are taken in communal dining halls. **[Maximum 3 marks]**

The Functions of Families

3. **Possible content: up to 4 marks for AO1; up to 4 marks for AO2; up to 4 marks for AO3.**
   - Define the term nuclear family and indicate that the traditional nuclear family is declining in statistical terms.
   - Draw on the functionalist perspective (e.g. Murdock and Parsons) to argue that the family performs essential functions for individuals and society.
   - Criticise the functionalist approach.
   - Draw on Marxist perspectives to argue that the nuclear family has an economic function which makes it essential to capitalism.
   - Criticise the Marxist approach.
   - Draw on feminist perspectives to argue that the nuclear family is essential to the workings of patriarchy.
   - Criticise the feminist approach.
   - Argue that attitudes to the nuclear family have changed and people now have more choice about how they organise their personal lives (e.g. living alone or remaining single).
   - Reach a balanced conclusion that addresses 'how far'.

The Marxist Perspective on Families

4. **Example answer:** Practical advantages in saving time and money. **[1]** In a group interview, the researcher would interview several married people together. They could gather a lot more data about attitudes to marriage and family life from a bigger sample of married people than with individual interviews, which are relatively time-consuming and expensive. **[3] Other possible advantages:** Accessing a range of views; interviewees may feel more comfortable/ empowered in a group setting; the group interview might generate fresh ideas – **1 mark for a relevant advantage and 3 marks for explaining this advantage.**

Feminist and Other Critical Views of Families

5. **Suggested answer:** Domestic violence, which can be seen as a form of power and control in which one family member tries to dominate others. This is usually – but not always – perpetrated by men and can be seen as a form of male power and control over women. **[Maximum 3 marks]**

Conjugal Role Relationships

6. **Example answer:** High-quality secondary sources on family life are readily available, which cuts down on the time and costs compared to gathering primary data. **[1]** A sociologist could access high-quality official statistics on family life in Britain today (e.g. marriage and divorce rates) and also draw on qualitative data from existing studies of family life carried out by reputable sociologists to save time and money. **[3] Other possible advantages:** Official statistics on marriage and divorce rates allow trends to be identified; research by other sociologists can provide a starting point for fresh research; secondary sources may be the only source available; can be used in the process of triangulation – **1 mark for a relevant advantage and 3 marks for explaining this advantage.**

7. **Suggested answer:** From a functionalist perspective, Parsons identified the instrumental and expressive roles in the nuclear family. The instrumental role belongs to the male (the husband/father) and involves working in paid employment outside the home, being the breadwinner and supporting the family financially. **[Maximum 3 marks]**

Changing Relationships Within Families

8. **Example answer:** Respondents have limited opportunity to develop answers. **[1]** A social survey contains pre-set questions, some of which are closed. The respondents do not get an opportunity to discuss parenting issues in their own terms, talk about their experiences of parenting in depth, raise new topics about the quality of parenting or explain why they ticked one box rather than another. **[3] Other possible disadvantages:** Qualitative data cannot be gathered; the researcher cannot deviate from the schedule of questions; the researcher has limited opportunity to build rapport – **1 mark for a relevant disadvantage and 3 marks for explaining this disadvantage.**

Changing Family and Household Structures

9. **Suggested answer:** A single-person household, i.e. one person who lives alone. This could be, for example, a young adult living in a bedsit, a person who is recently divorced or who never married, an elderly widow or widower living alone in the family home. The number of single-person households in Britain is rising. **[Maximum 3 marks]**

Marriage and Divorce

10. **B**
11. **Example answer:** One possible consequence is that the former partners may face loss of emotional support if their friendship groups change. **[1]** I would draw up a list of key points to cover in the unstructured interviews, e.g. friendship networks and social life during the marriage and after the divorce. I would select a small sample of divorced couples and obtain their informed consent. I would interview them and probe their answers about loss of emotional support in a sensitive way. I would then analyse the contents of the interviews, highlighting themes and relationships in the data, e.g. links between age, gender and emotional support after divorce. **[3] Other possible consequences:** Changes to their household setting; reduction in income; conflict over parenting and property – **1 mark for a relevant consequence and 3 marks for explaining how you would investigate this using unstructured interviews.**
12. **D**

The Role of Education from a Functionalist Perspective

1. **Example answer:** One function of the education system is secondary socialisation. **[1]** I would design an observation schedule that addresses secondary socialisation, focusing on the teaching and learning of norms and values during timetabled lessons. I would obtain informed consent before undertaking non-participant observation of a range of lessons in three different types of school. Next, I would analyse the data looking at similarities and differences in the socialisation of students in different types of school and identifying any patterns in the data related to students' gender, ethnicity or social class. **[3] Other possible functions:** Gender socialisation; economic function; selection; social control – **1 mark for a relevant function and 3 marks for explaining how you would investigate this function using observation.**

The Marxist Approach to Education

2. **Suggested answer:** From a Marxist perspective, Bowles and Gintis identify a connection or a close fit between school and work under capitalism. For example, at school, the hidden curriculum emphasises authority, rules and discipline. This fits with – and prepares students for – rules and discipline within the workplace. Through this correspondence, education creates a passive, obedient workforce to meet the needs of capitalism. **[Maximum 3 marks]**

3. **Possible content:** up to 4 marks for AO1; up to 4 marks for AO2; up to 4 marks for AO3.
   - Define the term capitalism.
   - Discuss conflict versus consensus approaches to the role of education in society.
   - Argue from a Marxist perspective that the main role of education is to produce a workforce for capitalism; discuss the work of Bowles and Gintis, and Willis.
   - Criticise the Marxist approach.
   - Argue from a functionalist perspective that education has several functions (economic; secondary socialisation; social control) and that education meets the needs of society.
   - Criticise the functionalist approach.
   - Argue from a feminist perspective that the main role of education is to reproduce patriarchy and gender inequality.
   - Criticise the feminist approach.
   - Reach a balanced conclusion that addresses 'how far'.

Different Types of School

4. **Suggested answer:** A public school such as Eton or Harrow. Public schools are independent of the state sector and are funded through the fees that parents pay. Many select their intake through an entrance examination. They market themselves on their academic ethos, traditions and varied extra-curricular activities. **[Maximum 3 marks]**

5. **A**

6. **Suggested answer:** Under the tripartite system introduced in 1944, students sit an 11-plus test at the end of primary school. Based on the results, they are allocated to one of three types of secondary school according to their aptitudes and needs. These are grammar, technical and secondary modern schools. Grammar schools have an academic focus. Technical and secondary modern schools have a more practical or vocational focus. **[Maximum 3 marks]**

Social Class and Educational Achievement

7. **Suggested answer:** How much of the right sort of cultural capital the parents have. Many middle-class parents who have been to university know how the education system works. They also know how to work the system (e.g. when applying for school places in outstanding schools) to maximise the chances that their children will perform well in exams and achieve their potential. **[Maximum 3 marks]**

The Impact of School Processes on Working-Class Students' Achievements

8. **Example answer:** To track changes in student behaviour in different bands over time. **[1]** With a longitudinal study, a researcher could carry out repeat interviews with one year group and their teachers in one school over time. They could focus on the Year 7 intake and track this cohort through to Year 11. The researcher could record any changes in students' behaviour and their attitudes to school over time, comparing the effects of banding on students in different bands. **[3] Other possible advantages:** The researcher can identify patterns in the data and connections between different variables over time; being able to follow up issues identified during previous stages; less reliance on people's memories; rapport building over time – **1 mark for a relevant advantage and 3 marks for explaining this advantage.**

9. **C**

Gender and Educational Achievement

10. **Suggested answer:** This refers to the idea that the traditional masculine identity of some men, such as young working-class men, is under threat. Traditionally, working-class masculine identity was linked to being the breadwinner and working in manufacturing and heavy industries such as shipbuilding. Today, many of these jobs have declined, so men are more likely to work in low-paid insecure jobs in the service sector. **[Maximum 3 marks]**

Perspectives on the Counter-School Culture

11. **A**

12. **Example answer:** Informed consent. **[1]** When researching sub-cultures in secondary schools, I must decide whether the younger students (e.g. those aged under 18) can give informed consent themselves. A member of a school sub-culture might want to take part in the study because they like the attention or the idea of appearing in a book but they might not appreciate any possible disadvantages, so I would deal with this by also asking the parents/carers to consent (or otherwise) on their children's behalf. **[3] Other possible issues:** Confidentiality; anonymity; avoiding harm to participants – **1 mark for a relevant issue and 3 marks for explaining this issue.**

Pages 17–21 Crime and Deviance

An Introduction to Crime and Deviance

1. **Example answer:** The family. **[1]** I would list the areas or points about informal social control in families that I wanted to cover in the interviews. I would identify a sample of middle-class and working-class families whose members would be willing to take part in the interviews about social control and get their informed consent. I would carry out the interviews. Once I had the interview transcripts, I would analyse the contents looking for themes, and similarities and differences between middle-class and working-class families in how social control operates. **[3] Other possible agencies:** Education; religion; peer groups – **1 mark for a relevant agency and 3 marks for explaining how you would investigate this agency using unstructured interviews.**

2. **Suggested answer:** Her Majesty's Prison Service. People who are found guilty of committing more serious crimes could get a prison sentence. The purpose of prison is to punish convicted offenders, rehabilitate them and deter them (and other people) from committing crimes in the future. **[Maximum 3 marks]**

Functionalist and Interactionist Perspectives on Crime and Deviance

3. **Example answer:** Explore the development of deviant careers over time. **[1]** A longitudinal study can investigate an issue over time. A deviant career involves several stages and takes time to develop. By using a longitudinal study, the researcher could identify a group of people who have been publicly labelled as deviant and track their lives over time to investigate why some of them develop deviant careers while others don't. **[3] Other possible advantages:** Building up rapport over time; obtaining a more detailed account of the process of developing a deviant career; participants' memories of events may be fresher – **1 mark for a relevant advantage and 3 marks for explaining this advantage.**

4. **C**

Marxist and Feminist Explanations of Crime and Deviance

5. **Suggested answer:** Women may be controlled at home through marriage, domestic life and motherhood. Many women who are mothers and wives/partners will have fewer opportunities and less time to commit crime than men if most of their time is taken up with domestic work, childcare, controlling children and emotion work. **[Maximum 3 marks]**

Statistical Data on the Extent of Crime

6. **Suggested answer:** The dark figure of crime refers to unrecorded crime – crime that does not appear in the police-recorded crime statistics produced by the state. The dark figure includes crimes without witnesses and unreported

crime. White-collar crime, for example, is more likely to be unrecorded than street crime. Some estimates suggest that official statistics include only a small proportion of all crimes committed. **[Maximum 3 marks]**

Factors Affecting Criminal and Deviant Behaviour

7. **Example answer:** As a researcher, I have a duty to safeguard the interests of all research participants (even if they belong to a deviant sub-culture) and to make sure they come to no harm as a result of the research. **[1]** If I observe the members of the sub-culture engaging in deviant acts or committing crimes, I must decide how to write these up in any publications. I would write them up in a way that safeguards the participants' identities; otherwise the members of the deviant subculture could be identified and penalised for taking part in the research. **[3] Other possible issues:** Informed consent; confidentiality – **1 mark for a relevant issue and 3 marks for explaining how you would deal with this issue.**

Other Factors Affecting Criminal and Deviant Behaviour

8. **Suggested answer:** The feminist sociologist Pat Carlen argues that working-class women are expected to make the class deal (as well as the gender deal). The class deal offers them material rewards such as being able to buy consumer goods if they work in paid employment for wages. However, if the rewards are not available or not worthwhile, the deal breaks down. **[Maximum 3 marks]**

9. A

10. **Possible content: up to 4 marks for AO1; up to 4 marks for AO2; up to 4 marks for AO3.**
    - Define the terms social class and criminal justice system (CJS).
    - Argue from a Marxist perspective that different social classes have different experiences of the CJS. Criminal law operates in the interests of privileged groups and, for example, benefit fraud is seen as more serious than tax evasion. The agencies of social control target street crime rather than white-collar or corporate crime. They also target working-class people.
    - Criticise the Marxist approach.
    - Argue from an interactionist perspective that different social classes experience labelling within the CJS differently. The police, for example, may label and target working-class people. Becker argues that some groups have the power to make the rules and enforce them. Power is related to social class, gender and ethnicity.
    - Argue from a feminist perspective that gender is more significant than class in influencing people's experience of the CJS. Men and women have different experiences of the CJS, e.g. through the chivalry effect and double deviance.
    - Argue that ethnicity is more significant than class, e.g. the police have been linked to institutional racism.
    - Reach a balanced conclusion that addresses 'how far'.

The Media and Public Debates over Crime

11. A

Pages 22–27 Social Stratification

An Introduction to Social Stratification

1. C

Different Views of Social Class

2. B

Factors Affecting Life Chances

3. **Suggested answer:** The glass ceiling refers to an invisible barrier in the workplace that stops women getting promoted to the top posts in industry, the legal profession, education, etc. This explains why men and women who work in the same profession are often found at different levels of the hierarchy, with men dominating the higher positions. **[Maximum 3 marks]**

4. **Suggested answer:** Introducing legislation to tackle racial discrimination at work by making it illegal and providing a means for people to challenge and stop it. In the 1970s, the Race Relations Act made racial discrimination illegal in employment. The Equality Act 2010 aims to promote a more equal society and outlaws discrimination based on race in employment. **[Maximum 3 marks]**

5. **Suggested answer:** The family is an agency of gender socialisation. Parents and other relatives distinguish between babies from birth according to their gender by dressing them in pink or blue and describing them in different ways. The term canalisation refers to the way parents channel their children's interests towards gender-appropriate activities, toys and games. **[Maximum 3 marks]**

Studies of Affluent Workers

6. **Example answer:** Inter-generational mobility. **[1]** I'd start by designing a questionnaire that asks respondents about their own social class background and career history, as well as that of their parents. Next, I'd identify a representative or typical sample of adults who would give informed consent and fill in the questionnaire. Once the questionnaires were completed, I'd analyse the data by looking for patterns of mobility according to social class, age, gender and ethnicity, and for any connections between these factors. **[3] Another possible type:** Intra-generational mobility – **1 mark for the relevant type and 3 marks for explaining how you would investigate this type using questionnaires.**

7. B

8. D

Wealth, Income and Poverty

9. **Example answer:** No control over the measurement of poverty. **[1]** As a secondary source, official statistics are put together by the state for administrative purposes rather than by sociologists for research purposes. The definition and measurement of poverty used by the state may be different from those a sociologist would prefer to use. As a result, the statistics might misrepresent and underestimate the true level of poverty in UK society. **[3] Other possible disadvantages:** lack of qualitative, in-depth data; the statistics tell us nothing about what poverty means to people – **1 mark for a relevant disadvantage and 3 marks for explaining this disadvantage.**

10. A

11. C

Different Explanations of Poverty

12. **Possible content: up to 4 marks for AO1; up to 4 marks for AO2; up to 4 marks for AO3.**
    - Define the terms divorce and poverty.
    - Outline which children are most vulnerable to poverty.
    - Argue from a feminist perspective that lone mothers have a high risk and long duration of poverty. Possible reasons include the gender pay gap.
    - Examine other possible reasons for child poverty such as the cycle of deprivation.
    - Argue from a Marxist perspective that child poverty results from class-based inequalities in capitalism rather than from rising divorce rates.
    - Argue that child poverty is linked to unemployment, welfare state inadequacies and globalisation rather than to rising divorce rates.
    - Reach a balanced conclusion that addresses 'how far'.

Power and Authority

13. **Example answer:** Paid employment. **[1]** Walby argues that the labour market segregates occupations by gender (e.g. fire fighters and nursery nurses) and women are in the worst jobs. Women typically earn less than men and are excluded from the better types of paid work. For many women, wages are so low that paid work is not really worthwhile in financial terms. **[3] Other possible structures:** The household; culture; sexuality; male violence; the state – **1 mark for a relevant structure and 3 marks for explaining this structure.**

Power and the State

14. **Suggested answer:** The police force. The police are an agency of formal social control in UK society and their role is to maintain order, enforce the law, investigate crime and apprehend people who break the criminal law. **[Maximum 3 marks]**

Pages 28–47 Practice Exam Paper 1

Section A: Families

01 C

02 A

03 **Suggested answer:** An empty nest family consists of a couple whose adult child or children have moved out of the family home (e.g. to set up their own home with a partner or to take up employment in another area). The couple now live together in a two-person family household. They are usually aged in their 40s, 50s or older, and may be retired. **[Maximum 3 marks]**

04 **Suggested answer:** One example of a dependent family member is a child aged 0–15 or aged 16–18 in full-time education. They live with their parent or parents, e.g. in a lone-parent or nuclear family. They have not yet completed their full-time compulsory education, are too young to be financially independent of their parents, and are likely to depend on their parents for emotional support. **[Maximum 3 marks]**

05 **Example answer:** One strength is that official statistics on divorce provide quantitative data that is collected on a national level from a reputable source following official standards and guidelines. **[1]** As a result, the statistics are likely to provide an accurate measure of divorce. **[1] Other possible strengths:** Reliability; generalisation is possible; can identify trends over time; an accessible and cheap source of data for sociologists studying divorce – **1 mark for a relevant strength and 1 mark for showing why this is a strength.**

06 **Example answer:** Higher expectations of marriage. **[1]** During that time, people began to expect more from their marriage. This was partly due to the way the media represented romance in films and pop songs. So people were no longer prepared to stay in a relationship that did not fulfil their hopes or needs. They were more likely to get divorced and possibly to look for fulfilment in a second marriage. **[3] Other possible factors:** Legal changes; less stigma attached to divorce; impact of secularisation; the changing social and economic status of women – **1 mark for a relevant factor and 3 marks for explaining this factor.**

07 **Example answer:** Explores how participants interact and respond to each other's views on arranged marriage. **[1]** The interviewer can explore how the interviewees respond to each other when they discuss their experiences of, and views on, arranged marriage in Britain. For example, do they support or dismiss alternative views, or does anyone change their mind about arranged marriage? This would provide an extra dimension over and above what would be possible in one-to-one interviews. **[3] Other possible advantages:** the ability to explore the theme of arranged marriage in depth; gather qualitative data; participants may feel more comfortable/empowered in a group setting; the focus group may generate new ideas about arranged marriage – **1 mark for a relevant advantage and 3 marks for explaining this advantage.**

08 **Suggested answer:** The research is based on secondary sources of information/a literature review. **[1]** Writing from a feminist perspective, Oakley uses pre-existing sources including the work of other sociologists. She uses the information to provide a critical analysis of the conventional nuclear family, including its financial inequality linked to gender. Oakley contrasts the idea of the conventional nuclear family with the reality and argues that living in conventional families can be stressful. **[3] 1 mark for identifying the relevant research method. Up to 3 marks for describing the method and the perspective.**

09 **Example answer:** One type of family diversity is social class diversity. **[1]** I would begin by noting down the themes or areas I wanted to cover in the interview, such as social class differences in role relationships and child-rearing practices. I would then identify a sample of working-class and middle-class couples who would be willing to give informed consent. I would carry out the unstructured interviews. I would analyse the interview transcripts by coding sections to identify any key themes, similarities and differences in conjugal roles and child-rearing practices between the social classes. **[3] Other possible types of diversity:** Cultural, life-course, cohort and organisational diversity – **1 mark for a relevant type of diversity and 3 marks for explaining how you would investigate this type using unstructured interviews.**

10 **Possible content: up to 4 marks for AO1; up to 4 marks for AO2; up to 4 marks for AO3.**
- Define the term gender inequality.
- Describe gender socialisation including canalisation within families as a source of inequality.
- Draw on feminist perspectives to argue that the nuclear family is the main source of gender inequality in society today. Discuss Delphy and Leonard's views on hierarchy and economic exploitation within families, and their views on patriarchy in families.
- Discuss inequality in power (e.g. decision making and domestic violence) in families.
- Draw on Sylvia Walby's feminist approach to argue that the family is one of several patriarchal structures in society, including paid employment, culture and sexuality.
- Criticise the feminist approach.
- Draw on Marxist approaches to argue that gender inequality within families is linked to the workings of capitalism rather than patriarchy. Men as well as women are oppressed under capitalism.
- Draw on the functionalist approach to argue that the nuclear family is functional rather than unequal. It meets the needs of individuals and society.
- Reach a balanced conclusion that addresses 'how far'.

11 **Possible content: up to 4 marks for AO1; up to 4 marks for AO2; up to 4 marks for AO3.**
- Define the terms function, nuclear family and primary socialisation.
- Draw on the functionalist perspective to argue that the main function of the nuclear family is the primary socialisation of children.
- Draw on Parsons' functionalist account of the two key functions: primary socialisation and stabilisation of adult personality.
- Describe other important functions of the nuclear family such as reproduction.
- Criticise the functionalist approach. Point out, for example, that some critics argue that many children are inadequately socialised within the family and/or that it is more relevant today to consider 'diverse families' rather than 'the nuclear family'.
- Draw on feminist approaches to argue that the main role of the nuclear family today is to reproduce patriarchy.
- Criticise the feminist approach.
- Draw on the Marxist approach to argue that the main function of the nuclear family is to reproduce capitalism.
- Criticise the Marxist approach.
- Reach a balanced conclusion that addresses 'how far'.

Section B: Education

12 B

13 D

14 **Suggested answer:** In a gendered curriculum, some subjects (including high status subjects such as maths and science) are associated with masculinity and others (such as languages and humanities) are associated with femininity. These ideas can influence (and limit) students' subject choices at school, their higher education course choices and future careers. **[Maximum 3 marks]**

15 Suggested answer: The social class system of stratification is based on achieved status. It is meritocratic and status is based on an individual's talents and abilities rather than their birth. Equal opportunities exist and working-class students can achieve qualifications through their own abilities, experience upward social mobility and get a middle-class job. **[Maximum 3 marks]**

16 Example answer: One strength is the size of the different samples. One sample had 2555 students and the other had 19 000 children. **[1]** The research covers a lot of students so the sample is more likely to be representative (compared to a smaller sample) or typical of the wider population of students. **[1] Other possible strengths:** Drawing on data from several sources; an opinion poll can be replicated to check the reliability of findings – **1 mark for a relevant strength and 1 mark for showing why this is a strength.**

17 Example answer: Impact of the economic recession on job opportunities. **[1]** Following the global recession and the limited job opportunities for young people, affluent parents might believe that there is more pressure on their children to achieve top grades in their GCSE and A Level exams in order to get into a prestigious university and enter a professional career. Affluent parents can afford to pay for private tuition as a way of investing in their children's futures during a recession. **[3] Other possible reasons:** More testing of students; more pressure to perform well in SATs; more pressure to pass the 11-plus exam/school entrance exam/ university entrance exam; increased competition within education – **1 mark for a relevant reason and 3 marks for explaining this reason.**

18 Example answer: The researcher is not in full control of the sample selection process. **[1]** Rather than select a random sample from school registers, snowball sampling means that the researcher has to rely on the willingness of secondary school students to identify their peers who truant. A student who truants might not want to identify other truants in case s/he gets them into trouble, or in case their parents/ teachers find out. This means that things like luck or chance play a part in the sample selection process. **[3] Other possible disadvantages:** Unlikely to generate a large sample; the researcher may not gather sufficient data; the sample will not be random/representative/typical of the wider population; the researcher cannot generalise – **1 mark for a relevant disadvantage and 3 marks for explaining this disadvantage.**

19 Suggested answer: Ball used participant observation as his research method. **[1]** He studied banding and mixed-ability teaching at Beachside Comprehensive School to explain the underperformance of working-class students. This was an ethnographic case study that focused on people in an everyday setting. Ball's perspective is partly interactionist because he explores the interactions between teachers and students but he also pays attention to the wider structure of the school. He is now a leading sociologist who studies social inequality within education. **[3] 1 mark for identifying the relevant research method. Up to 3 marks for describing this method and Ball's perspective on education.**

20 Example answer: One expectation is that students in the top band will achieve the highest grades at GCSE. **[1]** If teachers expect students in the top band to do well academically, this can act as a positive label. It could encourage these students to work harder than they otherwise would and strive for the top GCSE grades. The teacher could also push these students to improve their performance. In this way, high expectations could lead to a self-fulfilling prophecy in that the original prediction comes true. **[3] Other possible expectations:** Expecting students in the top band to complete a lot of homework; expecting students to prioritise school work; expecting students to stay on to study A Levels; expecting students to progress to university – **1 mark for a relevant expectation and 3 marks for explaining the impact of this expectation.**

21 Possible content: up to 4 marks for AO1; up to 4 marks for AO2; up to 4 marks for AO3.
- Outline the differences in educational achievements between students based on their social class, ethnicity and gender.
- Argue that students' family backgrounds are the most important factor. Examine the influence of factors linked to family backgrounds on educational achievement. Such factors include material deprivation, cultural deprivation, parental values and expectations, parents' educational backgrounds and cultural capital.
- Examine the influence of peer groups within the neighbourhood on educational achievement.
- Argue that school-based factors and processes are more important than family background. Examine the influence of factors such as teacher expectations, labelling and the self-fulfilling prophecy on different students' educational achievements.
- Examine the influence of school-based factors such as the school ethos, student cultures and anti-school sub-cultures on the achievement of different students.
- Argue that schools are meritocratic and that educational achievement is linked to individual effort.
- Examine factors such as school-based resources, the quality of teaching, the gendered curriculum and the ethnocentric curriculum on achievement.
- Argue that educational policy is most important. Examine factors linked to policy such as the impact of marketisation on different students and schools; the impact of equal opportunities policies and anti-discrimination legislation.
- Reach a balanced conclusion that addresses 'how far'.

22 Possible content: up to 4 marks for AO1; up to 4 marks for AO2; up to 4 marks for AO3.
- Outline the improvements in girls' educational achievements, such as their improved performance in public examinations; increased likelihood of progressing to university. However, subject choices within FE and HE are still gendered.
- Argue that these improvements are mainly due to feminism. Examine the impact of feminism on girls' attitudes to education, careers, gender roles and financial independence.
- Argue that the improvements are due to more girl-friendly schooling/the feminisation of education and changing assessment patterns such as coursework assessment. However, the curriculum is still gendered.
- Argue that the improvements are due to teachers' higher expectations of female students, labelling and the self-fulfilling prophecy.
- Argue that the improvements are mainly due to legislation/changing government policies such as the Sex Discrimination Act (1975), the Equality Act (2010) and the introduction of the National Curriculum.
- Argue that, despite the improvements, some feminists still see the education system as patriarchal.
- Reach a balanced conclusion that addresses 'how far'.

Pages 48–67 Practice Exam Paper 2

Section A: Crime and Deviance

01 B

02 C

03 Suggested answer: One example is sentencing policy and the sentencing of convicted offenders. People are not always clear about how sentencing works. For example, when offenders are released from prison early, people do not necessarily understand why this happens. The media sometimes fuel this public concern by reporting on early release prisoners who go on to commit further crimes. **[Maximum 3 marks]**

04 Suggested answer: Agenda setting refers to the media's power to set the focus of public debate about crime. The media do not tell people what to think but they do tell people what to think about. They do this by focusing on some groups and issues (such as illegal immigrants and street crime) and excluding others (such as corporate crime). Possible effects of this are that some groups become scapegoats, or the media create moral panics. **[Maximum 3 marks]**

05 Example answer: One strength is that John Williams was young, street wise and interested in football so he could successfully play the role of a football fan and undertake all three covert participant observation studies. **[1]** This allowed him to gather rich and detailed qualitative data about incidents of football hooliganism as they unfolded. **[1] Other possible strengths:** The research was covert so there is no observer effect; by doing participant observation, the researcher captures events first hand rather than relying on what people tell them in interviews; the researcher is able to see the world through the eyes of the hooligans – **1 mark for a relevant strength and 1 mark for showing why this is a strength.**

06 Example answer: The young men's socialisation within the home/neighbourhood. **[1]** The young men may have been socialised to value being 'macho' and to express their masculinity by drinking alcohol, vandalism and fighting with other men who they see as outsiders. So football is used as a context for fighting, violence and expressing masculinity. **[3] Other possible factors:** Status frustration among working-class males; peer group pressure; sub-cultural values and norms; fighting as a source of excitement and meaning; deviancy amplification in the media – **1 mark for a relevant factor and 3 marks for explaining this factor.**

07 Example answer: One disadvantage is the low validity of the responses. **[1]** Professional people in high status jobs might be unwilling to admit that they have been involved in undetected white-collar crime such as tax evasion or fiddling their expenses at work. Even though the researcher promises them anonymity and confidentiality, they may think it is not worth admitting any involvement because, if the truth came out, the consequences could be quite severe. In other words, they have nothing to gain and too much to lose by being honest in a self-report study. **[3] Other possible disadvantages:** Lack of opportunity to build rapport; lack of detailed, in-depth qualitative data; limited opportunity to explore the reasons behind white-collar crimes – **1 mark for a relevant disadvantage and 3 marks for explaining this disadvantage.**

08 Suggested answer: One response to success goals is innovation. **[1]** In this case, individuals accept the culturally defined goals (such as getting rich) but they lack opportunities to succeed through legal means. So these people innovate by turning to crimes such as theft or fraud to get rich. Merton examined the causes of crime and deviance from a functionalist perspective. He applied the concept of anomie (normlessness) to crime and deviance. He argued that if people experience a mismatch between the goals and the means, then the norms break down and people turn to any means available to achieve economic success. **[3] 1 mark for identifying a relevant response to success goals. Up to 3 marks for describing this response and Merton's perspective on crime and deviance.**

09 Example answer: One issue is the potential to cause distress to the research participants. Some victims of crime may feel upset or vulnerable when discussing their experiences. **[1]** These feelings may become more intense when taking part in research based, for example, on unstructured interviews. I would deal with this by explaining in advance what the questions are likely to involve, emphasising that participation is voluntary and that the participant has the right to withdraw from the research at any point without having to give a reason. **[3] Other possible issues:** Informed consent; anonymity; confidentiality; potential consequences for research participants such as being victimised for taking part – **1 mark for a relevant issue and 3 marks for explaining this issue.**

10 Possible content: up to 4 marks for AO1; up to 4 marks for AO2; up to 4 marks for AO3.
- Define the terms delinquency and socialisation.
- Draw on functionalist approaches to describe the importance of primary socialisation in families as a means of teaching norms and values. Argue that inadequate socialisation in families is the main reason for delinquency.
- Argue that other agencies of socialisation (e.g. religions and schools) are also failing to socialise children effectively and contributing to delinquency.
- Draw on Albert Cohen's sub-cultural theory to argue that delinquency among working-class boys is linked to status frustration at school rather than to socialisation at home.
- Argue that some sociologists do not focus on home factors. Interactionism, for example, focuses on the interaction between young people who commit delinquent acts and those who react to these acts.
- Draw on Marxist approaches to argue that certain groups (such as young people, particularly inner-city and working-class youth) are more likely to be targeted by the police and to be seen as delinquent.
- Reach a balanced conclusion that addresses 'how far'.

11 Possible content: up to 4 marks for AO1; up to 4 marks for AO2; up to 4 marks for AO3.
- Define female criminality and describe police-recorded crime statistics.
- Outline the gendered patterns of crime shown in police-recorded crime statistics: females commit fewer crimes, less serious crimes and are less likely to reoffend than men.
- Taking the statistics at face value, women may commit fewer crimes because they have less opportunity to offend. For example, their domestic role and triple shift mean they have less time to offend. Females are also more closely controlled than men.
- Taking the statistics at face value, it may be that gender socialisation processes encourage females to be passive and to avoid conflict and crime.
- Argue that the statistics underestimate the true level of female criminality because the police act with chivalry towards female offenders and treat them more leniently than males. So the police are less likely to arrest and detain female offenders and to record female crime. On the other hand, the double deviance theory suggests that women who commit crime (particularly women who do not conform to feminine stereotypes) are treated more harshly than men.
- Argue that police-recorded crime statistics are socially constructed and underestimate the level of crime committed by females, particularly middle-class females.
- Reach a balanced conclusion that addresses 'how far'.

Section B: Social Stratification

12 A

13 B

14 Suggested answer: One example of a social construct is gender. While sex (being male or female) is a biological construct, gender (masculinity and femininity) varies between cultures and over time. It is created by society through the process of primary socialisation in families. Gender is reinforced through secondary socialisation, e.g. through the gendered curriculum in schools. **[Maximum 3 marks]**

15 Suggested answer: The embourgeoisement thesis argues that affluent working-class families are becoming middle class in their norms and values due to an increase in their income and improvements in their standards of living. They now have privatised lifestyles centred on their home and family. **[Maximum 3 marks]**

16 Example answer: One strength is that the female researcher carried out a form of ethnography by wearing a niqab in public. This allowed her to gain direct experience of Islamophobia and to understand more fully how Muslim women experience this. **[1]** As a result, she could empathise with/build up rapport with the Muslim women and collect more in-depth and detailed accounts during the interviews. **[1] Other possible strengths:** The ethnography was covert so there is no observer effect; the researcher does not have to rely solely on what interviewees tell her in interviews; the ability to gather qualitative data that is likely to be valid – **1 mark for a relevant strength and 1 mark for showing why this is a strength.**

17 **Example answer:** Religious hate crime can affect people's life chances by affecting their health (including their mental health) in a negative way. **[1]** In this case, religious hate crime increased the women's chances of experiencing depression. If they are repeat victims of religious hate crime, this could affect their chances of being healthy or ill as they progress through life. **[3] Other possible ways:** Limiting the women's employment opportunities; limiting their opportunities to pursue higher education; contributing to their social exclusion – **1 mark for a relevant way and 3 marks for explaining this way.**

18 **Example answer:** Lack of flexibility. **[1]** Structured interviews are based on a pre-set schedule of questions and all interviewees answer exactly the same questions about their experiences of racism. If an interviewee raises a point about racism that the researcher had not anticipated, the interviewer cannot follow up this new line of enquiry by asking fresh questions about it. **[3] Other possible disadvantages:** The lack of opportunity to build rapport compared to unstructured interviews; lack of opportunity to gather detailed qualitative data about racism; potential for interview/interviewer bias – **1 mark for a relevant disadvantage and 3 marks for explaining this disadvantage.**

19 **Suggested answer:** The method was a large-scale questionnaire survey that was delivered face-to-face by a big team of interviewers across the UK. **[1]** This landmark survey asked about people's household resources and standards of living. Townsend developed a deprivation index to measure the extent of poverty (or relative deprivation) in the UK. He was a pioneer in the study of poverty because he focused on deprivation and viewed it in relative terms. **[3] 1 mark for identifying the relevant research method. Up to 3 marks for describing this research method and Townsend's perspective on poverty.**

20 **Example answer:** One group is elderly people, particularly older women. **[1]** Older people who rely on the state retirement pension may be at risk of poverty. They have to live on a relatively low income if they do not have an income from a workplace pension or a personal pension that they contributed to during their years at work. Older women are less likely to have built up an occupational pension than older men. **[3] Other possible groups:** Lone-parent families; women; some minority ethnic groups; children – **1 mark for a relevant group and 3 marks for explaining why this group is at risk of poverty.**

21 **Possible content: up to 4 marks for AO1; up to 4 marks for AO2; up to 4 marks for AO3.**
   - Define ethnicity and inequality.
   - Argue that ethnicity is the most important source of inequality by looking at issues such as racism, average earnings, average household income, unemployment, educational underachievement, poverty and the under-representation of some minority ethnic groups in positions of power in Britain.
   - Argue that some minority ethnic groups are better placed than others, e.g. in terms of educational achievement, so it is inappropriate to generalise.
   - Draw on Marxist approaches to argue that in capitalist society, social class is the most important source of inequality. Discuss issues such as working-class educational underachievement and life chances in relation to income, health, housing and social mobility.
   - Draw on feminist approaches to argue that gender is the most important source of inequality in patriarchal society. Discuss issues such as gender inequality at work, the glass ceiling, the gender pay gap, the risk of poverty, sexism and female under-representation in positions of power.
   - Argue that age and disability are the most important sources of inequality in contemporary British society.
   - Argue that all forms of inequality (including those based on sexuality) are significant and they should be seen as interrelated or linked rather than as separate aspects.
   - Reach a balanced conclusion that addresses 'how far'.

22 **Possible content: up to 4 marks for AO1; up to 4 marks for AO2; up to 4 marks for AO3.**
   - Define the term power.
   - Draw on the pluralist approach to argue that political power is distributed widely (e.g. through pressure groups, trade unions and direct action groups) and no single group dominates. The role of the state is to regulate the different interests in society.
   - Draw on the conflict approach to argue that power is concentrated in the hands of a minority whose members come from privileged backgrounds. Unelected groups such as chief executives of multinational corporations exercise power by influencing government policy.
   - Draw on Marxist approaches to argue that power in capitalist society is linked to social class relationships. Members of the bourgeoisie hold power based on their ownership of the means of production. The state protects the interests of members of the bourgeoisie.
   - Draw on feminist approaches to argue that power is concentrated in male hands in patriarchal society. Discuss Sylvia Walby's work on patriarchy in British society.
   - Reach a balanced conclusion that addresses 'how far'.

Notes

Notes

Notes

Notes

Acknowledgements

The author and publisher are grateful to the copyright holders for permission to use quoted materials and images.

Cover, p.1, © Rawpixel.com/Shutterstock.com, © zimmytws/Shutterstock.com, © tadamichi/Shutterstock.com
All other images © Shutterstock.com

Every effort has been made to trace copyright holders and obtain their permission for the use of copyright material. The author and publisher will gladly receive information enabling them to rectify any error or omission in subsequent editions. All facts are correct at time of going to press.

Published by Collins
An imprint of HarperCollins*Publishers* Ltd
1 London Bridge Street
London SE1 9GF

Content first published 2017
This edition published 2018

10 9 8 7 6 5 4 3 2

British Library Cataloguing in Publication Data.

A CIP record of this book is available from the British Library.

Authored by: Pauline Wilson
Commissioning Editors: Katherine Wilkinson and Charlotte Christensen
Editor: Charlotte Christensen
Project Manager: Tracey Cowell
Cover Design: Sarah Duxbury and Paul Oates
Inside Concept Design: Sarah Duxbury and Paul Oates
Text Design and Layout: Jouve India Private Limited
Production: Lyndsey Rogers
Printed in the UK, by Martins The Printers

MIX
Paper from
responsible source
FSC™ C007454
FSC
www.fsc.org

This book is produced from independently certified FSC™ paper to ensure responsible forest management.

For more information visit:
www.harpercollins.co.uk/green